Big Sharks
Of the
Carolina Coast

DISCARDED
from
New Hanover County Public Library

by
John Hairr

NEW HANOVER COUNTY
PUBLIC LIBRARY
201 CHESTNUT STREET
WILMINGTON, NC 28401

Averasboro Press

Published by
Averasboro Press
P.O. Box 482
Erwin, NC 28339

Copyright © 2003 John Hairr
All Rights Reserved
ISBN: 1-888879-48-3

Printed in the United States of America

NEW HANOVER COUNTY
PUBLIC LIBRARY
201 CHESTNUT STREET
WILMINGTON, NC 28401

Table of Contents

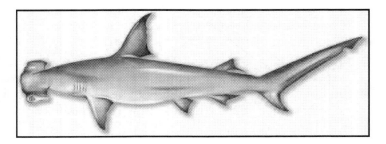

Great Hammerhead Shark
Photo courtesy NOAA

COVER PHOTO: Courtesy Bob Roush, North Carolina Aquarium at Fort Fisher.

Introduction

Before there were people, even before there were dinosaurs, sharks roamed the waters of our planet. Millions of years ago, when vast inland seas covered the coastal plains of what is now the southeastern United States and the Uwharrie Mountains were merely islands off an ancient coast, sharks swam about in search of prey.

Today, scientists estimate that there are approximately 400 species of sharks that prowl the world's oceans. Here in the waters off the Carolinas, from Currituck Beach in the north to Hilton Head in the south, approximately 60 shark species have been observed. These range from small sharks such as the spiny dogfish or the Atlantic sharpnose shark, up to the whale shark, the largest fish in the seas.

This publication discusses several of the larger shark species that have been found in the last two centuries along the shores of the Carolinas. These include sharks that are gentle giants, such as the aforementioned whale sharks, or the basking sharks. Also included are some very dangerous animals which have been known to kill people on very rare occasions such as tiger sharks, great hammerhead sharks, oceanic whitetip sharks, and the great white sharks.

One species included in this book is the sand tiger shark. Although not really one of the larger shark species inhabiting our waters, they are included here because sand tiger sharks are so often confused with the tiger shark. In addition, sand tiger sharks are frequently seen by tourists who come to

North and South Carolina, whether they be diving in shipwrecks off the Outer Banks or strolling through one of the aquariums along the coast that have sand tigers in their collections.

The final chapter of this publication is a historical overview of the shark attacks that have occurred along the coast of North and South Carolina. These are rare events, and not all have ended in a fatality.

Tail from a whale shark found in the Cape Fear River between Southport and Fort Fisher in June of 1934.

Photo courtesy NC Office of Archives and History

1. Whale Sharks

On the morning of June 5th, 1934, R.C. Fergus, a fish dealer from Wilmington, and his assistant were making a routine run down the Cape Fear River to Southport. As their boat churned through the waters of the river between Federal Point and Price's Creek, Fergus noticed an unusually large fin protruding above the water.

Upon closer inspection, the men discovered that the fin belonged to what they thought was a whale. Apparently, the beast had beached itself somehow on a sandbar in the river and perished. Closer inspection revealed a couple of deep cuts along the animal's body, apparently inflicted by the propeller of a boat, which appeared to be the cause of death. They measured the animal and found it to be forty feet long, with distinctive white spots on its back.

Realizing that people would doubt the veracity of a fish story of such huge proportions, Fergus decided to secure a line to the carcass in order to tow it ashore. There, Doubting Thomases and other curious onlookers could see the spectacle for themselves.

Despite their best efforts, their find remained firmly embedded on the sandbar. It was just too heavy for their small boat to move. They even noticed that not even the force of the tide had been able to budge it.

Fergus finally gave up on trying to move the behemoth, but he still needed to bring back proof of their find. Thus, the two men hacked off the beast's tail and a clasper. Fergus made careful measurements of the tail, which showed it to be nine feet, ten inches tall.

The items secure in their boat, the two men headed upstream and docked at the wharf along the Cape Fear at Carolina Beach. They hauled their trophies into town and put them on display for all to see.

Word spread quickly of Fergus' find, and it was not long before Louis T. Moore, then secretary of the Wilmington Chamber of Commerce, learned of the discovery. Moore had a friend that he knew would be extremely interested in this find, and immediately telegraphed the man telling him of the discovery.

Moore's friend was H.H. Brimley, the director of the North Carolina Museum of Natural History in Raleigh. A noted naturalist, he was keenly interested in all aspects of the state's natural history, and was constantly on the lookout for material to add to the museum's collection.

Moore's message stated that there was a large whale washed ashore near Southport which he could have for the museum. Wasting little time, Brimley left Raleigh and rushed to Wilmington, arriving early the next morning. There, he found Fergus, and the two men traveled down the river to have a look at the parts Fergus had left on display at Carolina Beach.

When they arrived in town that afternoon,

they found that the tail and clasper were gone. The town's health inspector had given the word that the rotting flesh had to go, so it was unceremoniously deposited in the town's garbage pile. The two men hurried to the dump and easily found the giant tail amidst the refuse.

Almost immediately, the naturalist Brimley was able to determine that the tail did not belong to a cetacean. "Definite identification was simple," he later wrote. "The sandpaper-like surface of the skin, the heterocercal tail, with its white spots, the side keels of the caudle peduncle, together with the enormous size of the tail, indicated that nothing but a large whale shark could have carried such an organ."

The whale shark, *rhineodon typus*, is the largest fish known, some specimens reaching sixty feet in length. These fish are usually found in warm, tropical waters and are seldom seen this far north. Brimley noted that prior to Fergus' find in the Cape Fear River, the most northerly point that a whale shark had been found in the Atlantic was on the east coast of Florida.

"Previous to this," Brimley wrote, "the most northern Atlantic point from which the species has been recorded was Ormond Beach, Florida, in 1902, Ormond being some three hundred and fifty miles south of the mouth of the Cape Fear River, which is in latitude approximating 34° N. The most northern Pacific record for the species is Cape Inubo, Japan, in latitude 35° 39' N. According to Dr. E.W. Gudger, this is the seventy-eighth recorded specimen, the seventy-seventh having been recorded recently by him from Acapulco, Mexico."

Modern readers might become alarmed after

learning that such a large shark was found in the waters of North Carolina, but it is important to realize that whale sharks do not eat people. They suck in their food while swimming, and feed on small fish, squid and crustaceans. They are known to eat while swimming in a vertical position, head raised to the surface and tail pointing downward. There are no reports of the frenzied feeding habits of other sharks. In fact, the whale sharks are so docile that some divers in the Indian Ocean take great delight in hopping on the backs of these giant fish, hanging onto the fins and riding through the water.

It is doubtful that such sport will ever catch on in North Carolina, however. The whale shark found by Fergus in the Cape Fear back in 1934 is the last known occurrence of this monster of the deep washing up on the shores of the North or South Carolina coast.

2. Basking Sharks

The second largest species of shark that inhabits the waters of coastal Carolina is the basking shark, *Cetorhinus maximus*. These sharks sometimes attain a size as long as 49 ½ feet long, but they rarely get more than 33 feet in length. The basking shark is second in size only to the whale shark, and thus has the distinction of being the second largest fish in the world.

In the North Atlantic, basking sharks prefer the cool waters of more northerly climes, but in the winter they migrate south to feed on plankton blooms. They are found in the coastal waters of the Carolinas during the winter months, usually in late winter as they work their way back toward the north to their preferred home in cooler waters off the coast of places such as Newfoundland, Iceland, or Great Britain.

As they cruise along the Carolina coast, basking sharks can often be seen feeding just offshore beyond the breakers. A basking shark feeds by opening its mouth and allowing large amounts of water to pass through its gills, where plankton and crustaceans are filtered out in its gill arches, much in the same manner as a baleen whale feeds.

The earliest documented account of a basking shark in the Carolinas was penned by Russell Coles in 1915. Coles nearly harpooned one off Cape

A basking shark taken off Corncake Inlet near Bald Head Island in February of 1935.

Photo courtesy North Carolina State Archives.

Lookout in July of 1905. Though he got within twenty yards of his prey, in this case the "big one" got away.

The first recorded taking of a basking shark along the Carolina coast occurred in February of 1935. A 13' 5" female was captured in a shad net near Corncake Inlet, just offshore from Bald Head Island. The shark was quickly gotten into the hands of H.H. Brimley of the State Museum in Raleigh, who studied it in detail, hoping to later reproduce a model of the fish for his collection. He pointed out that prior to this basking shark the most southerly occurrence of this species along the shores of the United States was at Sea Girt, New Jersey.

Brimley described the teeth and gills of this rare shark. "The teeth are numerous, recurved, and very small, with no cutting edges, the exposed part of the longest tooth being only about one sixteenth of an inch in length. The gill-rakers are highly developed and are used much as are the whalebone plates in the baleen whales, for straining from the water that flows into the mouth the small forms of marine life on which the animal feeds."

These sharks share another trait often associated with whales. On numerous occasions, basking sharks have beached themselves on the Carolina coast. For instance, in March of 2000 two basking sharks, measuring 25 feet and 28 feet, respectively, beached themselves within a 24 hour period on North Topsail Beach. Sometimes large schools of these fish beach themselves, as happened along the coast from Cape Hatteras to the Bogue Banks back in 1987 and 1988.

During the 20th century, several basking

Basking shark captured off Salter Path on April 25th, 1947. The shark is shown here in front of Ottis' Fish Market in Morehead City.

Photo courtesy North Carolina State Archives.

sharks were sited along the coast of the Carolinas. In North Carolina alone, Dr. Frank Schwartz counted 364 from 1901 through 2002. "Fishermen and the public accounted for 151 live sightings while 183 stranded basking sharks were measured between 1970 and 2000," wrote Schwartz.

In the spring of 1947, two basking sharks were caught by two different fishermen on the same day, April 25th, off the Bogue Banks. The first was taken near a place known as the Hoop Hole Woods by Captain Leo Gillikin of Morehead City. This shark, which measured 13 feet 6 inches long, was

A basking shark that died in a fisherman's net in Ocracoke Inlet on March 20th, 2002. Members of the US Coast Guard Group Cape Hatteras towed the animal's remains back to their station so scientists could study the rare shark.
Photo courtesy US Coast Guard Group Cape Hatteras

hauled into Morehead City and hoisted up for the curious onlookers to see.

The second basking shark was captured by Captain Gordon Lewis, also of Morehead City. His shark was approximately 13 feet long, and was taken approximately 2 1/2 miles away from the aforementioned basking shark. This basking shark was taken in 40 feet of water 2 miles off Salter Path. Captain Lewis brought his catch back to town, and put it on display at Ottis' Fish Market on the waterfront.

When writing a report about the two basking sharks taken off the Bogue Banks in 1947, E.W. Gudger observed that sharks of this species had been known to travel in small groups. "Being gregarious in its habits, it is said to loaf often in the sunshine in small companies. Several writers have noted that two or three will sometimes swim in tandem fashion with their dorsal fins high out of the water—each observed occurrence possibly giving rise to another sea serpent story."

Basking sharks are fairly docile creatures. Yet, despite their apparent harmless disposition, they can sometimes pose a threat to those who get too close. For instance, in the winter of 1999, a 38' fishing boat sank after colliding with one of these large sharks in the waters near the Frying Pan Shoals.

The boat was the *Bird Dog*, a sport-fishing boat that operated out of Carolina Beach. Her captain, Buddy Severt, and two crewmembers were cruising on calm waters about 18 miles southeast of Cape Fear when they inadvertently ran up on a basking shark floating along on the surface of the sea, apparently feeding. In the collision, the boat lost its running gear and had a big hole ripped out of her hull. The damage to the shark is unknown.

The sea raced in through the opening in the hull, quickly filling *Bird Dog* with water and causing her to sink. Fortunately, Severt and crew were able to make a fast escape into an inflatable raft. A distress call was made before abandoning ship, and a nearby fishing boat, the *Mike A Bee*, picked up Severt and his men. They were later transferred to another fishing boat, the *Class Action*, which was bound for Carolina Beach. Fortunately, all hands were safe despite their encounter with the second largest fish species in the ocean.

The *Bird Dog* has the distinction of being the only vessel in the Carolinas known to have been sunk by a shark.

It is a wonder more vessels did not suffer the same fate as the *Bird Dog*, as the seas around the Frying Pan Shoals were filled with basking sharks. Dr. Schwartz later received reports of a school consisting of 100 of these enormous fish that was observed on February 11th, 1999, in the vicinity of the Frying Pan and Cape Fear.

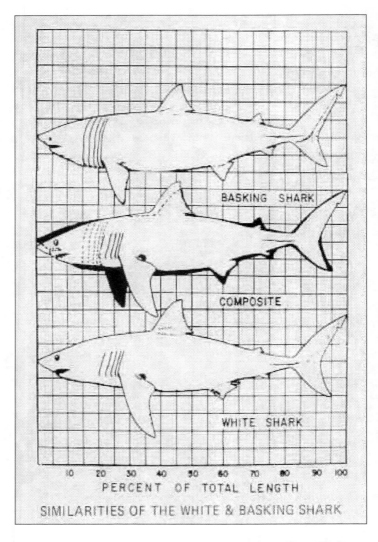

Photo courtesy NMFS-NOAA

3. Great White Sharks

Of all the big sharks that live in the ocean, none are as famous as the great white shark, *Carcharodon carcharias*. Books and movies abound chronicling the exploits of what some call "the Perfect Predator." Despite their popularity, few realize that great white sharks can be found here in the waters off the Carolina coast.

Great white sharks are normally associated with places that have relatively cooler waters such as California or New England. But great whites live in all of the coastal regions of the United States, including North and South Carolina. Here in the Carolinas, great whites tend to stay well offshore in the cooler, deeper waters. But under certain conditions they come closer to shore.

"What influences the great white's presence is winds," says Dr. Frank Schwartz. "If we have strong northwest winds, that will move the surface water offshore. This causes a reaction, pulling deeper, colder water from off the continental shelf onto the shelf, and the great whites come with it."

Like other sharks, great whites tend to be opportunistic feeders, and will avail themselves of whatever meat they can. They prefer to eat food with a high fat content, such as seals and whales. Younger great whites prefer to eat fish. As they get older, the larger sharks shift their preference to large mammals, and are known to have a taste for logger-head turtles. Female great whites tend to be larger than males.

On rare occasions great whites attack humans. These sharks have been responsible for many fatal encounters with people throughout the world.

Two shark attacks in the Carolinas have been attributed to great whites. One, which occurred off Atlantic Beach, North Carolina in July of 1957, was fatal. The other, which occurred off Pawley's Island, South Carolina back in 1961, was fortunately not fatal. However, the victim did lose an leg to the shark.

Great whites are the largest of the mackerel sharks. Some have been accurately measured in excess of 20 feet long. Many scientists today discount claims of great whites reaching sizes bigger than 30 feet in length. But there have been some claims of great whites reaching truly monstrous sizes, even off the coast of North and South Carolina.

The largest great white ever taken and accurately measured along the coast of the Carolinas was studied by Russell Coles back in June of 1918. The large shark had become tangled in a net off Cape Lookout. Coles' great white measured a remarkable 22 feet long.

One of the largest great whites ever seen off the Carolina coast was observed by Capt. Tony Austin about 15 miles off Emerald Isle back in 1988. The great white visited his fishing boat one evening as he and a friend were fishing for grouper. Austin maintains that this shark was as long as his 26 foot fishing vessel.

Large great whites have been encountered

A great white shark captured off the North Carolina coast, May 1984.

Photo courtesy North Carolina State Archives

off the Carolina coast as recently as January of 2004. Mark Beasenburg and Danny Mixon were returning from a fishing trip when they spotted an enormous great white approximately 10 miles off the entrance to Charleston Harbor. Beasenburg estimates that the shark was at least 23 feet long.

The most famous great white shark taken off the Carolina coast was caught in September of 1984 by Lloyd Davidson and the crew of the boat *Alligator*. In its day, this 2,080 pound great white was something of a media sensation. This was back in the days shortly after the movie *Jaws* had been released, so many people were curious to see one of these creatures up close. The shark's carcass went on display at Morehead City, and even put in an appearance at the North Carolina State Fair in Raleigh.

Today, the stuffed and mounted remains of the shark grace one of the walls of the North Carolina Maritime Museum at Beaufort. Though still quite imposing with its menacing teeth bared for all to behold, the display contains only about half of the shark's original 15.5 feet long body.

These sharks still make appearances along the Carolina coast. In the vicinity of Beaufort Inlet and Cape Lookout, Dr. Schwartz has noticed only a few large ones in recent years.

"We know about three big ones, 2 in 2001 and 2002, off on the other side of the shoals," says Dr. Schwartz, "and then about ten years ago we had 15 1/2 footer off the edge of the shelf. But the little ones, the eight footers, I see in April here off Beaufort Inlet."

Not all encounters with great whites in the Carolinas occur in the oceans. One recent encounter with a great white in North Carolina occurred in the Intracoastal Waterway near Wilmington. On December 12th, 1998, the body of a large shark was pulled ashore by the crewman from the Wrightsville Coast Guard Station. Bill Parker of the North Carolina Aquarium at Fort Fisher was called in to have a look at this large shark.

"We had a 14 foot 7 inch long total length female white shark," said Parker. "It was very large, 9 feet in girth around the pectorals."

The largest great white taken along the Carolina coast in recent years was caught by some fishermen out of Morehead City in April of 1986. According to Dr. Schwartz, this shark measured 15 feet 9 inches long, and weighed 2143.26 pounds. It was caught about 20 miles off the Bogue Banks.

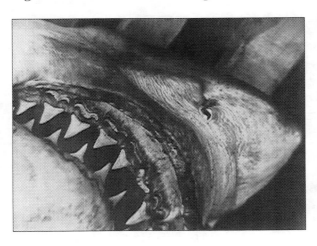

Teeth of great white shark landed by crew of the boat Alligator in September of 1984.

Photo courtesy Dr. Frank Schwartz
UNC Institute of Marine Sciences

Robert Keller poses with a record-breaking dusky shark he landed off Jennette's Pier at Nag's Head, North Carolina in 1963.

Photo courtesy Outer Banks History Center

4. Dusky Sharks

Dusky sharks, *Carcharhinus obscurus*, are frequent visitors to the Carolina coast, but little is known about them. They can grow to nearly 13 feet long, but on average they rarely exceed 10 feet, and weigh between 350 and 400 pounds.

These sharks have been observed in nearly all the oceans of the world. They prefer to live in deep water along the edge of the continental shelf, and rarely visit areas with lower salinity levels. They do come inshore to give birth to their young.

Pregnant dusky sharks have been observed by fishermen in the waters of Bulls Bay, South Carolina, in April and May. "The large size prevented bringing them on board their small boats for processing or bringing them to shore," wrote Dr. Jose Castro. "These fish were usually released by the fishermen if alive, or when dead, the large pups (up to 8 kg.) were removed and butchered. Thus, I only had the chance of examining a few term pups, and to confirm that gravid dusky sharks are present in Bulls Bay in late April and early May."

Thanks to shark tagging studies conducted in recent years, we now know that dusky sharks are capable of traveling great distances. Some sharks that have been caught and released off North Carolina have turned up later in the Gulf of Mexico off the Yucatan Peninsula. So far, none have been found to pass into the Pacific Ocean.

Because of their widespread distribution, dusky sharks are known by several interesting names throughout the world. These include bronze whaler, black whaler, bay shark, common whaler, dusky ground shark and shovelnose shark.

Dusky sharks are known to frequent the inshore waters of coastal regions. In 1973 and 1974, Melvin Huish and Christopher Benedict of the NC Cooperative Fisheries Research Unit studied the movements of dusky sharks in the Cape Fear River. After catching and tagging 10 dusky sharks with sonic transmitters, the fish were released and their activities studied. The sharks were caught and released in Snow's Marsh, across the river from the ferry terminal at Fort Fisher. "They did not remain near the place they were tagged and none crossed the river channel to the east side of the estuary," the scientists reported. "They also did not swim extensively in tidal creeks or the intake canal of the power plant."

A "Carolina" Sleigh Ride

In the nineteenth century, whalers out of Nantucket and other New England ports would often be dragged across the sea in their whaleboats for long distances by a whale that had been harpooned. The act of being towed by one of these whales is known in whaling folklore as a "Nantucket Sleigh Ride."

In North Carolina, there is at least one instance of people getting a free ride from a large marine animal that had been harpooned. But the obliging beast in this neck of the woods was a large shark.

The incident occurred on one of the sounds near Wilmington near the boat landing of Mrs. W.S. Willard back in 1938. Mrs. Willard's two sons and two of their friends, Joe Whitted and Christopher Quevedo, were rowing out on the sound when they spied a large shark. One of the boys flung his harpoon, which struck its mark.

The shark took off, towing the boat with the four boys across the water. The boys held onto the rope secured to the harpoon as the wounded shark made its way frantically down the sound.

The shark died before it could reach the open water of the ocean. The boys brought their catch ashore, and word spread of their fishing adventure. Soon, their prize shark was put on display a Gregg's Hardware Store in Wilmington. Unfortunately, we do not know what species of large shark this was that carried the boys on their memorable ride.

Byron Bass and friends at Toler's Cove Marina in Mt. Pleasant, South Carolina, pose with a record setting great hammerhead. Bass caught the shark in August of 1989.

Photo courtesy South Carolina Record
Marine Gamefish Program of the
South Carolina Department of Natural Resources

5. Hammerhead Sharks

With eyes fixed at the ends of their wing-like heads, hammerhead sharks look like some mythic beast dreamed up by a science fiction writer's fertile imagination. But these creatures of the deep are very real, and are frequent visitors to the shores of the Carolinas.

Hammerheads make up a family of sharks known as the Sphyrnidae. There are nine known species which make up the Family Sphyrnidae. These are the smooth hammerhead, small eye hammerhead, whitefin hammerhead, great hammerhead, bonnethead, scalloped hammerhead, winghead, scoophead and mallet head.

Of the nine species of hammerheads, four are found in the waters of the Carolina coast. These include the bonnethead, smooth hammerhead, scalloped hammerhead and great hammerhead. Three of the four species attain large size in our waters.

Bonnethead sharks, *Sphyrna tiburo*, are the smallest members of the Family Sphyrnidae found in the Carolinas. They are distinguished by their head, which is shaped more like a shovel than a hammer. They can grow up to five feet long.

Scalloped hammerheads, *Sphyrna lewini*, are found all along the Carolina coast throughout much of the year. According to Dr. Schwartz, scalloped hammerheads can grow up to 14 feet long. The largest scalloped hammerhead observed in the Carolinas was a little over 10 feet long.

The smooth hammerhead, *Sphyrna zygena*, are found in the waters of the Carolinas in the summer months. They can attain sizes up to 13 feet.

Many might be surprised to learn that the largest recorded smooth hammerhead from North Carolina was caught just off the waterfront of the port town of Beaufort in July of 1906. The shark was harpooned as it circled a fishing boat anchored out in Taylor's Creek less than 200 yards from shore. The shark was chasing a stingray when it was killed.

The next day, E.W. Gudger of the U.S. Fisheries Laboratory in Beaufort obtained the shark. He studied the fish and made careful measurements of the remains. He found the shark, which he classified as *Sphyrna zygena*, to be 12 feet 6 inches long. The length of the hammer between the eyes was 3 feet.

Perhaps most interesting is what he found inside the shark. "When dissected I found in the stomach an almost perfect skeleton of a stingray with many like fragments of other skeletons," wrote Gudger, "and I got from its throat, mouth and jaws 54 stings, varying from perfect spines to broken-off tips--souvenirs of at least that many stingrays, caught and probably eaten. But for all these accumulated stings, this shark was a living dynamo of energy when harpooned."

The great hammerhead, *Sphyrna mokarran*, is the largest of the various species of hammerhead sharks. Some have been observed that measured in excess of 20 feet long.

The hammer of the great hammerhead is straighter than other hammerheads, forming more of a straight line across the front of its head except for an indentation in the middle. Another distinguishing feature of these sharks are its teeth. A great hammerhead has triangular teeth with serrated edges. Dr. Jose Castro notes, "All the other hammerheads lack the strongly serrated teeth and the pelvic fins with curved rear margins."

The largest great hammerhead taken in North Carolina was a 13 feet 10 inch female. She was caught by Russell Coles off Cape Lookout back in July of 1918. Coles had observed the shark for two weeks.

In South Carolina, the largest great hammerhead ever landed was caught by Byron Bass in August of 1989. The shark measured 12 feet 7 1/2 inches long, and weighed 588 pounds 3 ounces.

The favorite food of great hammerheads are its fellow sharks and rays. Numerous fishermen down through the years have related finding stingray barbs lodged in the digestive track of a great hammerhead, a testimony to the last dying blow administered by a doomed ray.

Sometimes, these fish will even eat their own fellow hammerhead sharks. In 1919, Coles examined the aforementioned 13 feet 10 inch female great hammerhead. This female had eaten 50 juvenile great hammerheads from his net. She chose these victims despite the fact that sharks of other species were readily available.

Great hammerheads are regarded as potentially dangerous to humans, and have on occasion attacked people. But most encounters with these large fish do not lead to harm and injury.

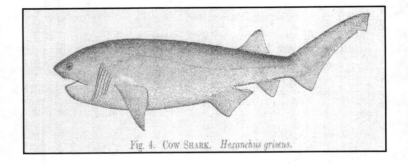

Fig. 4. COW SHARK. *Hexanchus griseus.*

Drawing of a cow shark from Fred Smith's *Fishes of North Carolina*, 1907.

6. Cow Sharks

At 3:00 a.m. on the morning of March 14th, 1886, a surfman patrolling the lonely shores of the northern Outer Banks of North Carolina noticed a large object in the surf. Unbeknownst to him, he had stumbled upon the remains of an infrequent visitor to the Carolina coast.

What he had found was a cow shark, *Hexanchus griseus*. These sharks are also widely known as sixgill sharks, as they sport six gill openings on each side of their body. These brownish colored sharks are often found in water over 6,500 feet deep, but are known to come close to the shore and surface on occasion.

Cow sharks are among the largest sharks in the ocean. Some have been observed that measured over 25 feet long.

When the surfman and his mates back at the Currituck Inlet Life Saving Station examined their mysterious fish, they noticed the creature's unusual teeth. What they may not have discerned was the shark's "third eye," a pale patch of skin on the top of a cow shark's head. Scientists today are unsure of the exact function of this "organ." Some theories maintain that since these sharks live so much of their lives in the abyssal depths, the light sensitive tissue is used to help them stay oriented properly with the ocean's surface.

Keeper D.M. Etheridge was intrigued and baffled by the unusual fish that had washed ashore near the Currituck Inlet station. He wisely decided to contact the U.S. National Museum to see if they would be interested in this odd find. That afternoon, he dispatched a telegram which read, "Awash. Fish unknown specimen was sent ashore three am ten feet long twenty one inches deep fourteen inches wide peculiar teeth."

Apparently the message piqued the interest of the folks at the museum in Washington and they relayed their interest back to Etheridge. On March 16th, 1886, he had the remains of his unusual fish crated up and placed aboard the steamer *Bonito*, bound for the nation's capital. The steamer made the journey in two days, and the shark's remains became part of the U.S. National Museum's collection on March 18th, 1886. T.H. Bean catalogued the specimen and officially identified the remains as *Hexanchus griseus*.

Once in Washington, the cow shark was measured and carefully studied. Next, a plaster cast was made and placed on exhibit in the museum.

The cow shark from Currituck Inlet remained on display for many years at what is now known as the Smithsonian Institution Museum of Natural History. Time, however, was not kind to the plaster casts that were utilized by museums throughout the world in those days. "Unfortunately very few of the old plaster casts of fishes still exist, and this one appears to have disappeared long ago," said Susan Jewett of the Smithsonian Institution.

Today, all that remains of the only cow shark ever found on the shores of the Carolina coast are pieces from its jaws and teeth. Fortunately, these are still being preserved at the Smithsonian.

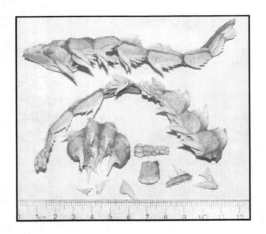

Fragments of the teeth and jaw are all that remain of the cow shark that washed ashore at Currituck Inlet in 1886.

Photos by Sandra J. Raredon of the
Division of Fishes, NMNH, Smithsonian Institution.

South Carolina Record Shortfin Mako, caught by Parker Ford south of Edisto Banks on April 21st, 2002.

Photo courtesy South Carolina Record
Marine Gamefish Program of the
South Carolina Department of Natural Resources

7. Mako Sharks

The shortfin mako, *Isurus oxyrinchus*, are large, fast fish that often weigh more than a thousand pounds. Though some have been observed that were over 13 feet in length, the average size of one of these sharks is between 8 and 11 feet.

Shortfin makos inhabit the tropical and temperate waters of nearly all the world's oceans. These fish frequent the shores of every continent except Antarctica. They are usually observed in the summer months off the Carolina coast.

Frequently observed by recreational water enthusiasts, the shortfin mako is one of the most widely known species of sharks. Many divers admire its sleek design and beauty as they gracefully glide past in the water. Sports fishermen regard it as perhaps the most invigorating shark to catch.

The largest mako caught in the waters of the Carolinas was taken by Russell Langford in 1983. The 768 pound, 8 ounce shark was taken off Oregon Inlet, North Carolina.

The state record shortfin mako caught in South Carolina waters was reeled in near Edisto Banks by Parker Ford on April 21st, 2002. The shark weighed 391 pounds, 15 ounces. The shark measured 9 feet 1/4 inch total length. Ford, a member of the Island Sportsman's Club on James Island, caught the shark on a Hatteras lure in 150 feet of water.

The mako put up a fight for two hours before he was landed.

Renowned for its acrobatic feats, these sharks are famous for their out of water antics. Often after being hooked, makos will make a desperate dash for freedom, and in the process leap high out of the water. They have been observed on numerous occasions making multiple jumps as much as 20 feet above the water's surface.

Equally impressive as their acrobatic skill is the speed of the shortfin mako, the fastest shark in the ocean. Many fishermen down through the years have attempted to accurately clock the speed of these sharks. There are claims that the shortfin mako can attain speeds as high as 46 miles an hour.

In addition to their athletic prowess, makos are also highly regarded for their mental capabilities. Some scientists believe the shortfin mako is the most intelligent species of all sharks. As shark expert Michael Bright notes, "the mako has the biggest brain for its body weight of any known shark."

Another interesting aspect of makos is that they have been known to make long journeys, sometimes in excess of 2,000 miles. On one occasion, a shortfin mako was caught, tagged and released off Cape Hatteras. The shark turned up four years later in the Gulf of Mexico off the Yucatan Peninsula. Where this shark had been during the intervening period is unknown, but a direct journey by sea from Cape Hatteras to Yucatan covers nearly 1,500 miles of sea.

Shortfin makos feed mainly on bluefish, mackerel and squid. If the opportunity presents itself, they have been known to eat birds and mammals as well.

The shortfin mako ranks 10th on the ISAF's list of shark attack species, with 12 unprovoked attacks on people between 1956 and 2000. However, the shortfin mako is the second leading species in attacks on boats, with 17 officially reported within the same time span.

There have been no records of shortfin makos attacking boats in recent years along the Carolina coast. However, there is a record of a shark attacking a boat that occurred off Southport back in September of 1895.

As the story goes, Robert Ruark, Hoyle Dosher and Elmer Adkins left Southport in an open boat and were fishing near the mouth of the Cape Fear near Fort Caswell. Dosher hooked a shark they

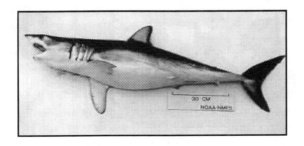

Shortfin Mako
Photo courtesy NMFS-NOAA

estimated to be five feet long. The shark did not appreciate being hooked, and charged the boat. When the fish struck the boat, Ruark was knocked overboard and landed, "a-straddle the shark's back." During the ensuing confusion, the shark broke free and made a dive for deeper water, with Ruark still on its back.

Ruark was rescued from sure drowning, if not an even more ominous fate, by grabbing the fishing pole that Dosher had extended out towards him. After the victim grabbed hold of the pole, Dosher and Adkins pulled their companion back into the boat.

Fishermen have to really be cautious with makos, as they have been known to take leaps out of the water and into boats after being hooked. As recently as June of 2001, a 7 1/2 foot shortfin mako jumped into a boat after being hooked about 30 miles off Ocean City, New Jersey.

Shark expert Thomas Allen described an attack by a school of makos upon a hapless boat carrying four men off the Australian coast several years back. "The men rowed frantically, but one of the sharks smashed into the boat, ripping a hole in it and hurling four men into the water. One man struck out for shore. He got about twenty yards before he was pulled under by a shark. Two others later disappeared and were never found. The fourth man lived."

So far, no incidents of this type have been chronicled from North or South Carolina.

8. Thresher Sharks

With their long, scythe-like tails, thresher sharks are some of the most easily recognized sharks in the ocean. Of the three species of thresher sharks that live in the world, two have been found in the waters off the Carolina coast—the common thresher, *Alopias vulpinas*, and the bigeye thresher, *Alopias superciliousus*. The latter lives is deep water and is seldom seen closer than seven miles offshore. But the common thresher is a regular visitor to our shores.

Sometimes referred to as fox sharks or whip-tail sharks, tales abound of the threshers' ability to corral and capture prey utilizing their distinctive tail. Unless a person has seen one of these sharks in real life, or seen actual photos of one of these fish, one might be tempted to believe that accounts of their herding and hunting prowess was based more on folklore than fact. Indeed, many of the stories may have been embellished down through the years. But enough of their antics have been witnessed and chronicled by experts and eyewitnesses to prove that the thresher shark is no coach whip snake of the seas.

Here is how shark expert Thomas Allen describes the thresher shark's antics. "The thresher pursues schools of mackerel, bluefish, shad, menhaden, bonito, and various herrings. When it nears a

This bigeye thresher shark was caught on November 7th, 1928, about a mile off Wrightsville Beach, NC.

Photo courtesy NC Office of Archives and History.

school of fish it splashes the water with its tail, driving the fish into a close-packed crowd and making smaller and smaller circles around them. Then, when the fish are jammed together in a frightened mass, the thresher darts among them, mouth agape, and swallows them. Sometimes threshers, working as a team, herd the fish between them and at the moment of slaughter share the meal."

Common threshers make their appearance in the fall of the year along the Carolina coast. Dr. Schwartz has observed these large sharks coming close inshore along the Bogue Banks. "We see them in November as they come in right along the beach

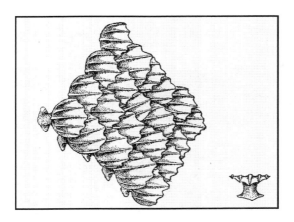

Instead of scales, sharks have denticles. This is a close-up drawing made by Lewis Radcliffe of the denticles from a thresher shark.

and go out past Swansboro, going south."

Common threshers were once prevalent along the shores of the Carolinas, especially in the area around Cape Lookout. In 1915, Russell Coles wrote that he had seen one in Cape Lookout Bight in July of 1914. "Although I was very close to it, I did not have my harpoons at hand and could not capture it," he wrote. "At the time of observation, it was feeding in shallow water by throwing the fish to its mouth with its tail, and I saw one fish, which it failed to seize, thrown for a considerable distance, clear of the water."

Today, these sharks are becoming a rare sight, and would seem to be facing a very bleak future. Researchers at Dalhousie University in Halifax, Nova Scotia, reported in 2003 that the population of threshers in the northwestern Atlantic Ocean had dropped by 80% since 1986. Whether this is a long or short term trend is not certain, but the scientists point out that the numbers for these sharks were already down in the 1980's from what had been observed back in the 1950's.

A thresher shark reeled in by an angler along the
Outer Banks. Note the size of the shark's tail in
relation to the rest of its body.

Photo courtesy Outer Banks History Center

Greenland Shark

Photo courtesy Dr. Steve Campana
Canadian Shark Research Lab.

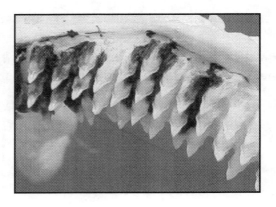

Close-up view of the teeth in the upper jaw of a Greenland Shark.

Photo courtesy Dr. Steven Campana
Canadian Shark Research Lab.

9. Greenland Sharks

Greenland sharks, *Somniosus microcephalus*, are some of the most enigmatic sharks in the sea. Unlike most shark species, they live predominantly in the cold waters of the polar and sub-polar regions of the Arctic. They are found at great depths, in excess of a mile below the ocean's surface.

When mature, these sometimes lethargic sharks average approximately 15 feet in length. Sometimes, they may grow as large as 24 feet long, and weigh over a ton. They can assume a variety of colors, including gray, brown, black or even purple. Some have white spots on their sides, while others may have dark bands.

One characteristic they do share with many other shark species is that they are not very discerning about what they eat. The Greenland shark's diet consists mainly of fish, but they will also eat hapless marine mammals if the opportunity presents itself. Bright notes that in the cold winter months, these sharks will eat just about anything that comes along, and points out, "parts of a horse, an entire reindeer (minus horns), and a seaman's leg complete with sea boot, have been found in the stomach."

For centuries, people inhabiting the Arctic regions of America and Europe took Greenland sharks and ate them. They are notoriously easy to catch, and put up little fight when hooked. Some

Eskimos are reported to have used blocks of wood for bait.

Though it may be easy to bring in, preparing the catch is a different story. Because of a chemical in the flesh, thought to be trimethylamine, the meat of these sharks is toxic. Those familiar with the preparation of this fish claim that it has to be boiled three times before it is fit for human consumption. Furthermore, if a dog drinks the water in which the fish is boiled, it will become terribly sick and might even die.

Greenland sharks are rarely encountered in the waters off the Carolinas, and there are no records of their having washed up on our beaches. Only two specimens have been observed in the waters offshore this far south. Dr. Frank Schwartz reports that one was taken off Cape Hatteras back in the 1980's.

In the early 1990's, Dr. Charles Herdendorf and several members of the Columbus America Discovery Group saw a large animal pass by the lens of their remote controlled camera. The camera was attached to a submersible nearly 7,500 feet deep on the bottom of the Atlantic Ocean approximately 150 miles east of Myrtle Beach, South Carolina. They were looking for artifacts relating to the *SS Central America*, a steamship that went down in a hurricane in 1857. What they saw that night was later identified as a Greenland shark.

10. Tiger Sharks

On September 3rd, 2001, a young couple from Russia were wading in the waters off Avon, North Carolina, when they were attacked by a large shark. Sergei Zaloukaev died of his wounds. His companion, Natalia Slobodskaya, was grievously wounded, but fortunately she managed to survive.

Dr. Jack Musick of the Virginia Institute of Marine Science investigated the attack. Upon studying the victims' wounds, he concluded that the guilty party was a tiger shark. He noted, "Given the size of the bite (at least 12" across) and the symmetrical nature of the bite and the apparent rolling behavior, the most likely species was the tiger shark (*Galeocerdo cuvieri*)."

Of all the large sharks that swim in the waters off the Carolinas, a species that poses an extremely high risk to humans along this stretch of coast is the tiger shark, *Galeocerdo cuvieri*. Many shark experts throughout the world categorize tiger sharks as one of the most dangerous sharks in the sea, more of a threat than even the legendary great white.

The upper portion of the tiger shark's body ranges from gray to brown, while the portion underneath is white, gray or even yellow. When young, a tiger shark's skin is covered with black blotches. As the shark matures, the blotches stretch into long, faint stripes that resemble the stripes of a tiger, hence the name.

They are the largest members of a family of sharks known as requiem sharks. Tiger sharks, on average, are believed to grow to somewhere between 13 and 15 feet long. But some tiger sharks have been caught that measured in excess of 20 feet long, and weighed more than a ton.

Thanks to shark tagging studies, we now know that tiger sharks can travel great distances, in some instances swimming thousands of miles to waters off the continents bordering the Atlantic Ocean. One researcher noted, "These fish showed movements from North Carolina to south and east of the Flemish Cap, and west of the Spanish Sahara; from Georgia to the Cape Verde Islands; from Bimini to New York."

A tiger shark was caught and released off Cape Hatteras in January of 1996. He turned up in the summer of 1997 1,549 nautical miles away.

The earliest reliably documented account of a tiger shark off the Carolina coast dates back to 1885. On July 30th of that year, J.N. Maffitt and J.A. Corbett were fishing off the mouth of the Cape Fear River when they spotted a large shark. One of the men had brought along a rifle, and used it to shoot the shark. After bringing it back to Southport and examining the body, it was determined that they had killed a tiger shark. The shark was, "10 feet long and 5 feet in circumference, and weighed 400 pounds." The men skinned the shark, and kept the skin as a souvenir of the encounter.

Though definitely a threat to humans, tiger sharks appear to be far more dangerous to other sharks than to people. On numerous occasions in

The photo above shows the tiger shark caught by Walter Maxwell off the Cherry Grove Pier near Myrtle Beach, South Carolina, on June 14th, 1964. The record-breaking fish was 20 feet long, and weighed 1,780 pounds.

Photo courtesy Cherry Grove Pier.

the waters off the Carolinas, tiger sharks have been seen engaging in acts of cannibalism against other sharks, including other tiger sharks.

Lewis Radcliffe, of the U.S. Marine Fisheries Laboratory at Beaufort, North Carolina, witnessed a cannibalistic attack from the deck of his boat, the *Fish Hawk*, back in August of 1914. While in the Fort Macon Channel of Beaufort Inlet, Radcliffe noticed a small school of these fish swimming around his boat, so he decided to try to catch one. He quickly hauled in 3 tiger sharks, measuring 8 3/8 feet, 10 ½ feet and 9 1/6 feet, respectively. As he was hoisting the third catch on board, another tiger shark rushed up and tried to deprive him of his prize.

> "About this time a shark, larger than any of those taken, swam up to the one hanging from the boom, and raising its head partly out of the water, seized the dead shark by the throat. As it did so, the captain of the *Fish Hawk* began shooting at it, with a 32-caliber revolver, as rapidly as he could take aim. The shots seemed only to infuriate the shark, and it shook the dead one so viciously as to make it seem doubtful whether the boom would withstand its onslaught. Finally it tore a very large section of the unfortunate's belly, tearing out and devouring the whole liver, leaving a gaping hole across the entire width of the body large enough to

permit a small child to easily enter
the body cavity. At this instant one of
the bullets struck a vital spot, and after a lively struggle on the part of the
launch's crew, a rope was secured
around its tail"

Upon his return to Beaufort, Radcliffe laid
out his sharks for measurement and study. His
fourth and final tiger shark measured out to 12 feet
long. Inside its stomach were 40 pounds of the un-
digested remains of the third tiger shark's liver. Inside one of the other tiger sharks was a rat, while
another had the remains of an unidentified shark.

Tiger sharks are not too finicky when it
comes to getting a meal. British author Michael
Bright, who refers to tiger sharks as "the ocean's
dustbin with fins," compiled the following list of
items which have been consumed by tiger sharks.

"At one time or another, rubber
tyres, a roll of tar paper, a roll of
chicken wire, a bag of potatoes, a
sack of coal, beer bottles, plastic
bags, a tom-tom drum, pork chops,
hamburgers, lobsters, trousers, horns
of deer, cloth rags, glass bottles,
leather shoes, tennis shoes, sea
snakes, squid, unopened tins of
green peas and salmon, cigarette
tins, an artillery shell casing, bag of
money, explosives, pet cats and
dogs, parts of dolphins, porpoises
and whales, other sharks, stingrays,

and a variety of land and sea birds
have been found in the stomachs of
tiger sharks…"

South Carolina has been known for many
years for its large tiger sharks. One example was a
large shark caught by John Gardner from the pilot
boat four miles off the Charleston Jetties on July
18th, 1940. Gardner hooked his shark, and after
what was described as, "about an hour's terrific bat-
tle," managed to bring in the shark. Once it was
alongside the boat, a rope was secured to the fish,
and it was hoisted up with a block and tackle, an op-
eration that took five men to perform because of the
enormous weight of the fish. Gardner carefully
measured the shark, which he found to be 15 feet 2
inches long.

Gardner took photographs of the shark, and
gave them to E. Milby Burton of the Charleston Museum. Burton identified the shark as a tiger shark.
He also did some research, and found that this was
the largest tiger shark recorded from the Western
Atlantic Ocean. The man who caught this monster
shark was not really impressed. "Strangely enough,"
wrote Burton, "Mr. Gardner did not think the shark
of such an unusual size as to warrant particular attention."

A tiger shark has the distinction of being the
largest fish ever caught from a fishing pier along the
Carolina coast. At Cherry Grove Beach on the
northern South Carolina coast, Walter Maxwell of
Charlotte, North Carolina, was fishing from the
Cherry Grove Pier on June 14th, 1964, when he
landed a tiger shark of enormous propensities.

There were no scales in this rural coastal town large enough to accurately weigh this monstrous fish, which measured 20 feet in length. So the next day, the shark was placed on a truck and driven to the nearby town of Loris, where an adequate set of scales was found. Maxwell's tiger shark weighed 1,780 pounds, a world record that still stands today. Witnesses aver that had the shark been weighed right after it was taken, and not allowed to dry out on the beach for a day, the weight would have been even higher.

Two years later and a few miles up the coast, Maxwell caught another record-breaking tiger shark. This one was taken off the Yaupon Beach Pier, and weighed 1,150 pounds, 8 ounces. This set a record for a tiger shark caught in North Carolina that has never been eclipsed. Thus, Maxwell has the distinction of holding the record for the largest tiger sharks taken in both North and South Carolina.

Sand Tiger Shark

Photo courtesy Daryl Law
NC Aquarium on Roanoke Island

11. Sand Tiger Sharks

Because of a similarity in names, people frequently confuse tiger sharks and sand tiger sharks, but these are two very different species of sharks. Sand tiger sharks, *Carcharias taurus*, are on average about half as big as tiger sharks. Whereas the tiger shark will eat just about anything, sand tigers normally eat fish and other sea animals such as crabs, octopus and squid.

They are also considered to be much less dangerous than tiger sharks are to humans, at least off the coast of the Carolinas. Many tourists come each year to dive with sand tiger sharks off such wrecks as the tanker *Papoose*, which was sunk off Cape Lookout by a German U-boat in World War II. In Australia and South Africa, where they are known as both gray nurse sharks and ragged tooth sharks, they have a more fearsome reputation.

In October of 1983, diver Roderick Farb discovered a shipwreck in the Atlantic Ocean off Ocracoke, North Carolina, which proved to be the elusive wreck of the submarine, the *USS Tarpon*. Study on this and subsequent dives showed that the wreck is frequented by large numbers of sand tiger sharks.

As time passed, more sand tiger sharks were found at other dive sites in the area. Scientists now realize that the warm waters south of Cape Hatteras and west of the Gulf Stream down to Cape Lookout are frequented by sand tiger sharks for breeding purposes. The numerous sharks teeth which divers like Farb have reported finding on the wrecks on the ocean's bottom in this area attest to the often violent behavior meted out between sand tiger sharks while frequenting the waters off the southern Outer Banks.

The most distinguishing feature of a sand tiger shark is its menacing teeth. The spike shaped teeth protrude in an irregular fashion from its mouth.

The largest sand tiger shark caught along the North Carolina coast was taken by Derrick Dove on Portsmouth Island on October 17th, 1998. This shark was 8 1/2 feet long, and weighed 325 pounds.

The largest sand tiger shark taken in the waters off South Carolina was caught at Charleston by Mark Thawley in 1993. According to officials at the International Game Fishing Association, the 350 pound 20 ounce sand tiger landed by Thawley is a world record.

The previous world record for a sand tiger shark was set by a Mr. D. Wolfe at Nag's Head, North Carolina. His fish weighed 318 pounds, and measured 8 feet, 3 inches long.

Sand tiger sharks are frequently seen in aquariums around the world. This is because they have proven hardy and can adapt to living in captivity. Many species of sharks, such as the great white, will die if kept in an aquarium. But sand tiger sharks rarely fail to adapt if given proper care and fed adequately. Most aquariums feed their sharks on a regular schedule and supplement their diets with vitamins.

The North Carolina Aquarium on Roanoke Island, the Ripley's Believe It or Not Aquarium in Myrtle Beach, and the South Carolina Aquarium in Charleston, all have exhibits featuring live sand tiger sharks.

12. Oceanic Whitetip Sharks

Prowling the open seas well offshore, Oceanic whitetip sharks, *Carcharinus longimanus*, have gained a bad reputation for being a threat to victims of tragedies on the high seas. Since they inhabit the far offshore realm, they are seldom seen, but on those unfortunate occasions when an airplane goes down in the ocean or a ship sinks, these large sharks turn out in force to feast on the victims.

Some oceanic whitetips grow as large as 13 feet long. Most, however, are believed to be around 7 or 8 feet long. They are so named because of the white tips of their tail and fins, which stand out in contrast to their brownish color.

The sharks often live in large schools. According to Bright, a school consisting of hundreds of these sharks was seen off the Massachusetts coast back in 1941. "According to deep-sea fishermen," he wrote, "the further from land they are seen, the more numerous they become."

Oceanic whitetips are found in the world's oceans well offshore from land. Though some occasionally find their way as far north as Canada, they prefer areas where water temperature stays warmer than 70° F.

These sharks are found in the waters off the Carolina coast, but to see them a person has to head for deep water. Dr. Schwartz observed that they are found in the area all year long, "in waters deeper than 183 m (100 fm)."

In 1965, Charles Bearden noted that seven of these sharks had been taken by the RV *Oregon* the previous year. He wrote, "The only records which could be found for the whitetip shark off South Carolina were far offshore near the edge of the continental shelf. "

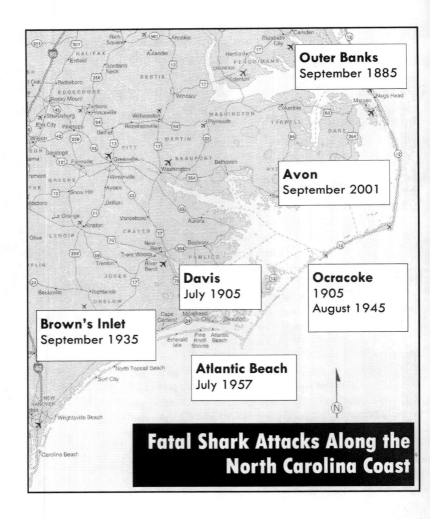

Outer Banks
September 1885

Avon
September 2001

Davis
July 1905

Ocracoke
1905
August 1945

Brown's Inlet
September 1935

Atlantic Beach
July 1957

N

Fatal Shark Attacks Along the North Carolina Coast

13. Shark Attacks Along the Carolina Coast

The most dangerous part of a visit to the beaches of the Carolinas is the drive down on the crowded highways. If a person survives the harrowing trip, hazards such as being struck by lightning, drowning or being caught in a rip current pose real threats to a person's wellbeing. All of these calamities are much more likely to end a person's life in coastal Carolina than an encounter with a shark.

Shark attacks have occurred in all of the North Carolina counties bordering the Atlantic Ocean, from Currituck south to Brunswick County. The majority of cases come from the waters of New Hanover County, though none of the incidents in the latter county have proven fatal.

In South Carolina, shark attacks have been experienced all up and down the coast from Myrtle Beach to Hilton Head. Most of the attacks have been in the vicinity of Charleston. This probably has more to do with the fact that historically there have been more people in and on the water at this busy seaport city than at other locales across the state.

It should be noted that the true number of shark attacks that have actually occurred in the waters of the Carolinas is probably higher than the number officially recorded. There are a couple of reasons for this. One is the likelihood that several incidents went unrecorded because of the remote nature of the region. The other reason is that many incidents of shark attacks were quickly downplayed by those responsible for promoting the region to tourists.

In the 1930's, E. Milby Burton, Director of the Charleston Museum, became curious about why there were so few authentic shark attack records from the Atlantic coast of the United States. He set out to find out if there were any incidents along the South Carolina coast that had gone unrecorded. By examining hospital records and interviewing several individuals, he chronicled seven shark attacks that happened between 1907 and 1933 He heard rumors of several others, but was unable to authenticate the attacks.

Burton noted some of the difficulties he encountered in his research. "Invariably when an attack of this kind occurs every one immediately concludes, 'barracuda.' In many respects this is quite understandable, as the psychological effect would be extremely bad and no one would frequent the bathing beaches...The great barracuda (*Sphyreana barracuda*) is apparently very rare in and around Charleston."

Since Burton's article, there have been numerous shark attacks documented from the South Carolina coast. None were fatal. But some did gain widespread attention, such as the attack on two men swimming at Folly Beach back in 1938.

On July 13th, 1938, Harvey Haley, a 45 year

old school superintendent from Hot Springs, Arkansas, and his friend, William Tanner, were wading in the surf in three feet of water nearly 100 yards offshore when a shark seized Tanner's ankle. Tanner managed to hold his ground with his free foot, and beat the shark about the head with his fists. Haley, who was six feet away when the attack occurred, reached out to his friend and grabbed him by the wrist. A tug of war ensued between Haley and the shark, with Tanner playing the part of the rope. Haley felt the shark underneath his feet, and kicked it, at which point the shark released its grip and swam away. Haley then helped his friend ashore, and shortly thereafter found medical assistance. Tanner's foot was severely injured, but luckily the doctors managed to avoid amputation.

Word of Haley's heroic struggle to save his friend spread fast. On January 24th, 1940, Haley was awarded a medal for bravery from the Carnegie Hero Fund Commission.

So far, the earliest documented shark attack in the Carolinas occurred in Charleston Harbor back in the summer of 1837. A young boy who was part of the crew of the ship *Plymouth* had a close call with a shark after jumping into the waters off a place described as "Magwood's wharf."

A writer from the *Charleston Courier* chronicled the event:

> **"The young man, it appears, had gone into the water to bathe, and while under the water, saw a monstrous Shark, making at**

him open mouthed; he exerted himself to rise to the surface, and in so doing came in contact with his assailant, and gave him a blow on his *knowledge box*, which caused him to retreat, and the youth then made for shore. The Shark then attacked him in the rear, and seized his right foot, and nearly succeeded in biting off two of his toes, but the gallant young sailor used his left foot with so much energy as to cause him to lose his hold. The young man then gained the wharf, and gathering up his clothes, went on board the vessel, leaving the monster *breakfastless*. We saw the courageous young son of Neptune, a very short time after the occurrence, sitting upon the deck of the ship, and he related the circumstance with as much coolness as if he had been only a witness, instead of an actor in the dangerous encounter. We are pleased to learn from the physician who dressed the wound, that there is every prospect that his toes will be saved."

In North Carolina, the earliest documented shark attack occurred in the Cape Fear River off Smithville (modern Southport) back on July 26th, 1870. Several members of Battery G, 4th Artillery, were swimming in the Cape Fear River opposite

Fort Johnson when bugler Giles Gordon had his foot seized by a shark. Shortly thereafter a witness described the scene. "When the shark first seized the bugler, it drew him beneath the surface of the water; but, by the violent exertions of the disentangled leg, he tore the other foot from the grasp of the terrible monster and swam a few feet to the wharf, when he was assisted out of the water and taken to the hospital."

Fortunately for the victim, medical attention was only a short distance away. The Post Surgeon was able to dress the wound and save the man's mangled foot. Giles, who at the time was being discharged from the service as his enlistment term had expired, convalesced at Fort Johnson before heading home.

On rare occasions, shark attacks in the Carolinas have been fatal. According to the International Shark Attack File of the American Elasmobranch Society at the Florida Museum of Natural History in Gainesville, Florida, there have been 3 fatalities in the waters off North Carolina since 1935.

The earliest recorded fatal shark attack in North Carolina predates the ISAF's records by half a century. This incident occurred in the waters off the Outer Banks back in the summer of 1885. Details are sparse, but in September of that year, the body of Frank Hines of Edenton, NC washed up on shore. A newspaper account from the time noted, "The general impression is that he was struck by shark while bathing in the surf."

Nearly 20 years would pass before another fatal shark attack was recorded. This one occurred in the waters of Core Sound near Davis. In July of

1905, a 16 year old boy named Sutton Davis was playing in waist deep water when he was seized by a shark. A contemporary newspaper account described the incident. "Sutton was in water about waist deep when suddenly a shark approached him, threw him in the air and caught him as he struck the water, pulled him under and disappeared in deep water with the boy." No trace of the body was ever recovered.

At roughly the same time as the shark attacks in Davis, there were two other shark fatalities in Carolina waters. Both occurred just across Pamlico Sound at Ocracoke. Dr. Schwartz chronicled the two fatalities, one of which happened sometime between 1900 and 1905, and the other which occurred in 1905.

The next fatal shark encounter in North Carolina occurred at Brown's Inlet in Onslow County, in the fall of 1935. The site where the incident occurred, between Topsail Island and Hammock's Beach State Park, is now a part of Camp Lejeune Marine Corps Base.

On September 21st, 1935, Jere Fountain, Jim Collins and Paul Venters, all of Onslow County, were camping on the island between the mouth of New River and Bear Inlet. About 8:30 p.m., the men decided to go swimming in the waters of Brown's Inlet. As they were wading in waist deep water, Fountain called out to his companions for help, as something had bitten him.

Venters quickly made his way to his wounded friend, and helped him up onto the beach. Try as they might, neither Venters nor Collins were able to stem the flow of blood coming from a grievous wound just above the knee in Fountain's leg. Jere Fountain quickly bled to death there on the sandy beach overlooking Brown's Inlet.

The *New Bern Tribune* later wrote of Fountain's wounds. "The leg was nearly severed above the knee. Coroner Kimmon Jones stated he was certain that prints of a shark's teeth were on Fountain's body."

Fountain left behind a widow and three children.

Almost a decade later, another individual lost their life in an encounter with a shark off the North Carolina coast. Once again, this attack took place at Ocracoke. On August 6th, 1945, a crewman from the Coast Guard station there on the island decided to take a swim in the Atlantic Ocean in his off duty hours. Unfortunately, he was attacked and killed by a shark. The incident occurred on the beach near where the Ocracoke Airport is located today. His body was taken to New Bern and buried in the Federal Cemetery.

The next deadly shark attack in the waters off North Carolina occurred on July 15th, 1957, off Atlantic Beach in Carteret County. Rupert Wade, a 57 year old resident of Morehead City, was a renowned long distance swimmer who often amazed the tourists at the local beaches with his swimming stamina. On this occasion, he was over 1,000 feet offshore swimming with Billy Shaw, an 18 year old lifeguard. After about 15 minutes in the water, Wade yelled out to his companion that a shark had bitten him, and told Shaw to swim for shore and get help.

The Coast Guard was immediately summoned, and sent a 30 foot boat from Fort Macon.

The boat carried Seaman Kerry Lewis and EN2 Earl Taylor. Lewis was the first to spot Wade floating on the water. Two individuals who had swum out from shore to render assistance-David Lee and Mike Robinson, joined them. Lewis dove in, and the men helped Wade, who was alive but unconscious, into the boat.

Once they were all aboard, they set out for Fort Macon, where they were met at the dock by an ambulance. But despite the fact that they administered artificial respiration on the trip back, they were unable to revive Wade, who was pronounced dead at the Morehead City hospital. He bled to death as a result of the wounds inflicted by the shark.

The death of Wade was attributed to the work of a great white shark. He was bitten on the right leg midway between his hip and knee, ripping deep enough into his flesh to expose the bone in his leg. He also had several deep cuts on his right foot.

The year 2001 was one of those rare years in which North Carolina suffered a fatal shark attack. On September 3rd, 2001, a young Russian couple was wading in the waters off Avon in the Outer Banks when they were attacked by what is believed to have been a tiger shark. The man, Sergei Zaloukaev, died of his wounds. His fiancé, Natalia Slobodskaya, lost her foot to the shark, but survived the ordeal.

This shark attack incident drew considerable media attention because of the fact that it was one of two fatal shark attacks that occurred over the Labor Day weekend. On September 1st, 2001, 10 year old David Peltier was mortally wounded by a bull shark while swimming with his family at Virginia Beach,

Virginia. Two days later and 130 miles down the coast, Zaloukaev and Slobodskaya were attacked at Avon.

According to the International Shark Attack File, there have been 3 confirmed fatal shark attacks in the waters of South Carolina, all of which took place in the 1800's. Two of these incidents, in 1840 and 1852, occurred in Charleston Harbor. The other occurred at an unspecified location along the South Carolina coast back in 1883.

Experts are unsure why sharks attack humans. Most believe that shark attacks are cases of mistaken identity.

Regardless of why sharks attack people, it should be remembered that these attacks on humans, especially in the waters of North and South Carolina, are very rare events.

Bibliography

Allen, Thomas B., *Shadows in the Sea*. The Lyons Press, 1996

Baum, Julia K. et. al., "Collapse and Conservation of Shark Populations in the Northwest Atlantic," *Science*, 299:389-392, January 17, 2003.

Bearden, Charles, *Elasmobranch Fishes of South Carolina*. Bears Bluff Laboratories, 1965.

"Bitten By A Shark," *Wilmington Daily Journal*, July 31, 1870.

Bright, Michael, *The Private Life of Sharks*. Stackpole Books, 2000.

Brimley, H.H., "Basking Shark (Cetorhinus Maximus) In North Carolina Waters," *Journal of the Elisha Mitchell Scientific Society*, 51:311.
--"Notes on the Occurrence of a Whale Shark (Rhincodon Typus) in the Cape Fear River, Near Southport, N.C.", *Journal of the Elisha Mitchell Scientific Society*, 51:160-162.

Brown, Aycock, "Maneaters Rare Off Coast," *News and Observer*, May 28, 1950.

Burton, E. Milby, "A Record Tiger Shark From South Carolina," *Copeia*, 1941 (1) 40-41.
—"Shark Attacks along the South Carolina Coast," *Scientific Monthly*, March, 1935.

Casey, J.G. and N.E. Kohler, "Long Distance Movements of Atlantic Sharks From the NMFS Cooperative Shark Tagging Program," *Discovering Sharks*, S.H. Gruber, ed., American Littoral Society, 1990.

Castro, Jose, "The shark nursery of Bulls Bay, South Carolina, with a view of the shark nurseries of the southeastern Untied States," *Environmental Biology of Fishes*, 38:37-48, 1993.

—*The Sharks of North American Waters*, Texas A&M University Press, 1983.

Coles, Russell J., "The Large Sharks of Cape Lookout, North Carolina. The White Shark or Maneater, Tiger Shark and Hammerhead," *Copeia*, 69:34-35, 1919.

--"Notes on the Sharks and Rays of Cape Lookout, N.C.," *Proceedings of the Biological Society of Washington*, Vol. XXVIII, 89-94, April 13, 1915.

Farb, Roderick, *Shipwrecks Diving the Graveyard of the Atlantic*, 2nd ed.. Menasha Ridge Press, 1998.

"Fight With A Shark," reprinted from *Charleston Courier* in *The Standard*, September 9, 1837.

"Funeral For Shark Attack Victim," *New Bern Tribune*, September 24, 1935.

Gudger, E.W., "The Basking Shark, *Cetorhinus Maximus*, On the North Carolina Coast," *Journal of the Elisha Mitchell Scientific Society*, 64:41-44, June 1948.

--"Sizes Attained by the Large Hammerhead Sharks," *Copeia*, 1947 (4) 228-236.

--"The Tiger Shark, *Galeocerdo Tigrinus*, On the North Carolina Coast and Its Feeding Habits There," *Journal of the Elisha Mitchell Scientific Society*, 64:221-233, December 1948.

Henry, Michael, "25-foot Shark Snared by Net, Dies," *Outer Banks Sentinel*, 23 March 2002.

Holloman, William, "The Real Jaws," *The State*,

August 1986.

Huish, Melvin T. and Christopher Benedict, "Sonic Tracking of Dusky Sharks in the Cape Fear River, North Carolina," *Journal of the Elisha Mitchell Scientific Society*, 93(1), 28-36, 1977.

Lee, Morgan, "Basking Shark Sinks 'Bird Dog'," *Wilmington Morning Star*, February 26, 1999.

Musick, Jack, "Details of the Attacks, September 1-3, 2001," *Report of the Virginia Shark Attack Task Force*, Fall, 2001.

Radcliffe, Lewis, "The Sharks and Rays of Beaufort, North Carolina," *Bulletin of the U.S. Bureau of Fisheries*, 34:239-384, 1914.

Reaves, Bill, "Sharks of North Carolina," Unpublished manuscript, Bill Reaves Collection, New Hanover County Public Library, 2000.

Schwartz, Frank, "Basking Sharks, Cetorhinus maximus, Family Cetorhinidae, Recorded In North Carolina Waters 1901-2002," *Journal of the North Carolina Academy of Science*, 118(3) 202-205, 2002.
—"Elasmobranchs of the Cape Fear River," *Journal of the Elisha Mitchell Scientific Society*, 116(3), 206-244, 2000.
—"Food of Tiger Sharks, Galeocerdo Cuvier (Carcharhinidae) From the Northwest Atlantic Ocean, Off North Carolina," *Journal of the Elisha Mitchell Scientific Soceity*, 116(4), 351-355, 2000.
—*Sharks, Skates and Rays of the Carolinas*, UNC Press, 2003.

Schwartz, Frank and George H. Burgess, *Sharks of North Carolina and Adjacent Waters*. North Carolina Dept. of Natural and Economic Resources, Division of Marine Fisheries, 1975.

"Siezed By a Shark," *Wilmington Messenger*, July 30, 1905.

Smith, Hugh M., *The Fishes of North Carolina*. Bulletin of the N.C. Geological and Economic Survey, 1907.

"Tiger Sharks Travel Long Distances," *The Shark Tagger 1997 Summary, Newsletter of the Cooperative Shark Tagging Program*, 1997.

Top Five Species For
Unprovoked Shark Attacks
From 1580-2000

	Species	# Unprovoked Attacks
1.	Great White Shark	254
2.	Tiger Shark	91
3.	Bull Shark	66
4.	Sand Tiger Shark	37
5.	Blacktip Shark	32

Based on statistics compiled by the International Shark Attack File

DISCARDED
from
New Hanover County Public Library

ABOUT THE AUTHOR: JOHN HAIRR is an award-winning author with several books to his credit, including *South Carolina Lighthouses*; *Colonel David Fanning*; and *Outer Banks*. He has spent several years researching the interactions between people and their environment along the coast of the southeastern U.S.. In addition to his written works, John has directed several documentary videos, including *Lighthouses of the Cape Fear Coast* and *Great White Sharks of the Carolina and Georgia Coast*.

310 M9 FM 1.06
08/01/05 166010 SELF